The Letter in the g

n nice sunny days, the Lettermen liked to work in their garden.

As usual there was a lot of digging to do, which was very hard work. Not all of the Lettermen liked to dig quite as hard as they should have done, as you can see.

s they dug, they woke up lots of wriggly worms in the earth, who popped up the say hello, before wriggling off to find somewhere else to sleep.

When the earth was nicely dug, the Lettermen decided to plant some seeds. They hoped these would all grow into lovely flowers, which would make their garden very pretty.

After they had planted the seeds, they had to sweep the path.

As it hadn't been swept for a long time, it was rather messy.

And guess what was growing up between all the stones...

The Lettermen had to pull up the weeds before they could get on with any more work. If you've ever tried pulling up weeds, you'll know how difficult it is.

They put the weeds in a big pile with all the garden rubbish they'd collected, and made a bonfire. This would get rid of everything in the Lettermen's garden which they didn't want. And maybe something they did...

You see, the Lettermen had built their bonfire too close to the shed where they kept all their garden tools. And just look what was happening...

After all that excitement, the Lettermen noticed the grass on their lawn had grown rather long. So they got out their old mower and cut the grass nice and short, which was much better for playing on later.

hey put the grass cuttings into a big pile. This looked so soft and comfortable and all that gardening had made the Lettermen so tired, that they were soon fast asleep.

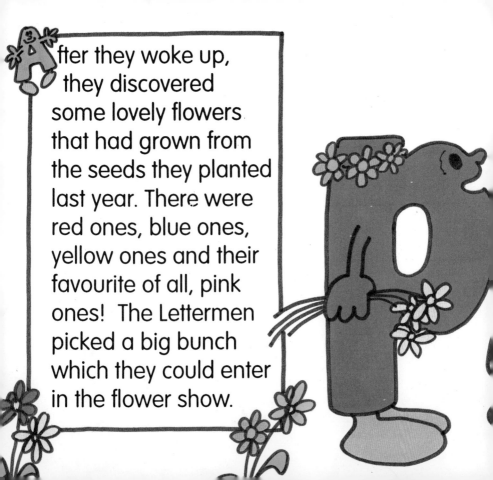

After they woke up, they discovered some lovely flowers that had grown from the seeds they planted last year. There were red ones, blue ones, yellow ones and their favourite of all, pink ones! The Lettermen picked a big bunch which they could enter in the flower show.

he Lettermen arranged the flowers in their nicest vase. Because with flowers as beautiful as these, they were sure of one thing..